JUDGE DREDD GRAPHIC PAPERBACKS

CAPED CRUSADER CLASSICS

TITAN BOOKS

JUDGE DREDD
vs. THE DARK JUDGES

written by
John Wagner
drawn by
Brian Bolland

JUDGE DREDD VS THE DARK JUDGES
ISBN 1 85286 109 6

Published by
Titan Books Ltd
58 St Giles High St
London WC2H 8LH

This edition first published September 1988
10 9 8 7 6 5 4 3 2 1

Cover illustration by Brian Bolland.
Colouring by John Burns.

Judge Dredd appears weekly in *2000 AD* and is © Fleetway Publications 1988.
This edition is © Titan Books Ltd, 1988.

This volume contains the stories *Judge Death* (*2000 AD* Progs 149-151) and *The Dark Judges* (*2000 AD* Progs 224-228).

Printed in Great Britain by Cox and Wyman, Reading, Berkshire.

JUDGE DEATH

IN MEGA-CITY ONE, GIANT METROPOLIS OF THE 22ND CENTURY, A CRIMINAL WAS ESCAPING FROM THE LAW...

DUMB JUDGES! HA! THEY'LL NEVER CATCH TINY THE TAP!

ULP! ME AN' MY BIG MOUTH! I-I SURRENDER, JUDGE!

SCRIPT: JOHN WAGNER   ART: BRIAN BOLLAND

WHEN THE BODY WAS FOUND, TOP LAWMAN JUDGE DREDD WAS CALLED IN —

IT'S TINY THE TAP! WE WERE CHASING HIM WHEN WE LOST HIM IN THIS MAZE.

WHEN WE FOUND HIM HE WAS DEAD. THERE'S NOT A MARK ON HIM — BUT LOOK AT HIS FACE!

LIKE HE DIED OF... TERROR!

NO SIGN OF ANY ATTACKER, BUT WE FOUND THIS UNDER TINY'S NAILS. COULD BE SKIN TISSUE. PONGS A BIT!

THERE'S A STRANGE SMELL OF DECAY ALL AROUND HERE. OKAY, RUN THAT DOWN TO THE LAB. I'LL GET A SEARCH SQUAD OUT.

SOON, AT THE LAB—

SKIN, ALL RIGHT. MIGHT BE HUMAN—HARD TO TELL JUST YET. IT'S IN AN ADVANCED STATE OF *DECOMPOSITION...*

I'M NOT TALKING ABOUT DAYS, OR EVEN YEARS. THIS SKIN HAS BEEN DEAD FOR *CENTURIES.*

IMPOSSIBLE. IF THE SKIN ISN'T TINY'S, IT'S GOT TO BE HIS ATTACKER'S.

THEN ALL I CAN SAY IS —
WE'VE GOT A MIGHTY STRANGE
KILLER WALKING THIS CITY!

HE HEARD THE SOUND ECHOING THROUGH THE CONCRETE CAVERNS OF THE CITY. IT DREW HIM LIKE A MAGNET...

THE ONE SOUND WHICH COULD STIR *FEELING* IN THAT COLD, DEAD HEART. THE SOUND OF LAUGHTER...OF *LIFE*...

THAT HATED SOUND!

LAWBREAKERS! YOU HAVE *DELAYED* ME, THAT ISS ALL. THISS CCITY ISS EVIL, BUT *I* WILL CLEANSSE IT!

ALL WILL BE JUDGED!

THE REMAINS WERE TAKEN TO THE MORGUE. THERE, DREDD CALLED IN PSI-DIVISION — JUDGES SPECIALLY TRAINED FOR THEIR *ABNORMAL PSYCHIC POWER*...

THAT'S JUDGE ANDERSON, OUR BEST OPERATOR. IF ANYONE CAN *CONTACT* THIS CREATURE, SHE CAN.

I'D BETTER FILL YOU IN, ANDERSON...

SAVE YOUR BREATH. I'VE ALREADY *READ* YOU. CAN'T HIDE YOUR GUILTY *SECRETS* FROM A *TELEPATH*, YOU KNOW!

I HAVE NO GUILTY SECRETS.

SO THIS IS OUR MYSTERY JUDGE, EH? YOU WANT ME TO GET IN TOUCH WITH HIM SO YOU CAN ZAP HIM WITH A FEW VERBALS... OKAY, ON WITH THE SHOW!

MUST SHE BE SO FLIPPANT?

PSI-JUDGES ARE HIGHLY-STRUNG. SHHHH!

THE CHARRED SKELETON HELPED ANDERSON LINK WITH THE CREATURE—

IT'S OUT THERE SOMEWHERE... I CAN FEEL IT! GOT TO REACH OUT—

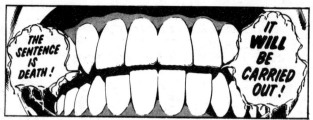

THE SENTENCE IS DEATH!

IT WILL BE CARRIED OUT!

JUDGE DEATH BROKE CONTACT —

A CREATURE FROM A WARPED WORLD WHERE LIFE IS A CRIME!

LOSING HIS BODY CRIPPLED HIM. HE NEEDS SOMETHING... OR SOMEONE... BUT I COULDN'T BREAK DOWN HIS BARRIERS TO FIND OUT WHAT.

SO ALL WE CAN DO IS WAIT—AND HOPE WE'LL BE READY FOR HIM. OKAY, ANDERSON, GET SOME REST. I MIGHT NEED YOU AGAIN.

TRY NOT TO MAKE IT A NIGHT CALL NEXT TIME. SEE YOU LATER, ADJUDICATOR.

I'M BEAT. THAT CREEP'S MIND POWER WAS STRICTLY *OVERLOAD*. HE MUST BE WORKING ON DIRECT CURRENT.

DON'T GO TO SSLEEP, ANDERSSON...

THAT VOICE AGAIN!

OPEN THE WINDOW, ANDERSSON. LET ME IN!

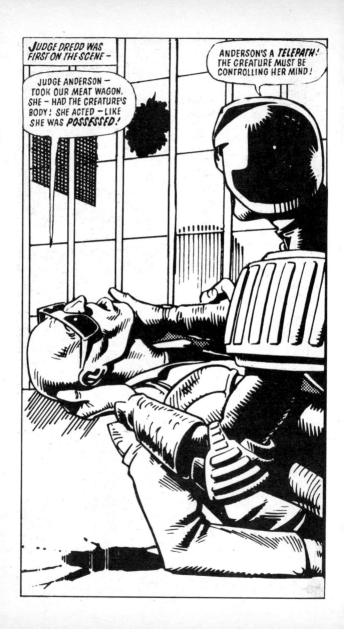

...*FIGHT HIM!*

AT THE HALL OF JUSTICE, OTHER *PSI-DIVISION TELEPATHS* WERE LISTENING FOR MESSAGES FROM ANDERSON...

JUDGE DEATH'S TRYING TO STOP HER TRANSMITTING — BUT ANDERSON WON'T *QUIT!* SHE'S HEADING EAST ON CHARLES ATLAS BRIDGE!

AND THERE'S ANOTHER THING, JUDGE DREDD...

IT'S VERY INDISTINCT, BUT IT'S COMING THROUGH TIME AND TIME AGAIN. JUST ONE WORD... "*BOING*"!

BOING? YOU MEAN THE MIRACLE SPRAY?

ON THE FOURTH FLOOR —

THIS IS THE PLACE. I'LL HANDLE HIM ALONE. WHEN I'M INSIDE, *SEAL* THE DOOR. I WANT IT *AIRTIGHT!*

THE MIRACLE PLASTIC SWELLED AROUND ANDERSON —

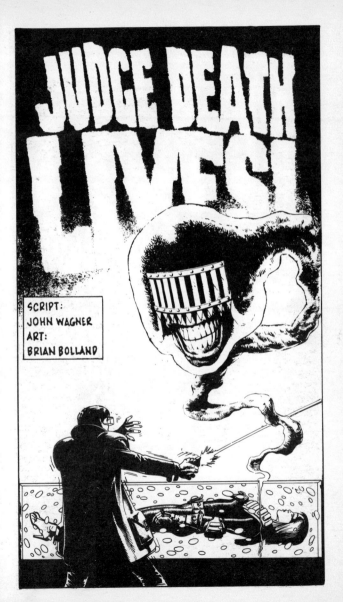

UNAWARE OF THE TERRIBLE CONSEQUENCES OF HIS ACT, THE MAN WHO FREED *JUDGE DEATH* HURRIES TOWARDS HIS APARTMENT IN *BILLY CARTER BLOCK* —

APT 1027B

J-JANINE !

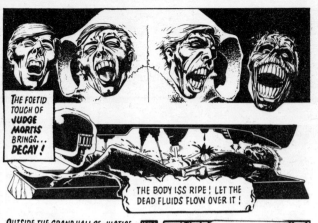

THE FOETID TOUCH OF **JUDGE MORTIS** BRINGS... DECAY!

THE BODY ISS RIPE! LET THE DEAD FLUIDS FLOW OVER IT!

OUTSIDE THE GRAND HALL OF JUSTICE —

JUDGE DREDD, YOU'RE HEADING THE SEARCH! JUST WHAT **HARM** CAN THIS MONSTER DO?

ACCORDING TO THE WARPED LOGIC OF HIS DIMENSION, ALL CRIME IS COMMITTED BY THE LIVING — THEREFORE LIFE **ITSELF** IS A CRIME.

AS LONG AS JUDGE DEATH IS AT LARGE, NO CITIZEN IS SAFE!

BUT YOU SAY HE'S IN SOME KIND OF... SPIRIT FORM?

HE CAN CREATE ANOTHER BODY. HE WILL TRY TO. THAT'S ENOUGH QUESTIONS!

ATTENTION, **JUDGE DREDD!** SOMETHING INTERESTING HERE! ONE OF THE HALL OF HEROES TOURISTS IS REGISTERED AS HAVING **STRONG TELEPATHIC POTENTIAL** – POSSIBLY A **CARRIER** FOR **JUDGE DEATH!**

NAME OF MITSON. APARTMENT 1027b, BILLY CARTER BLOCK.

ON MY WAY!

ENTER, **DEATH!** FILL THIS **SOULLESS CARCASS!**

AAAAAH!

TERRIBLE CARNAGE, DREDD! MUST BE FIFTY DEAD ON THE SHIELD — AND THEY KEEP COMING!

FIFTY! DON'T TALK TO ME ABOUT **FIFTY**, OBENG!

IT'S THE OTHER **SEVENTY THOUSAND** IN THAT BLOCK I'M WORRIED ABOUT!

THE SSSHIELD !

IN PEANUT PARK, JUDGE DEATH ALSO SENSES THE DANGER —

THE SSSHIELD !

MANTRAP!

GAZE INTO THE **FACE OF FEAR!**

FOR A MOMENT THE ICY CHILL OF TERROR COURSES DOWN DREDD'S SPINE. THE SHOCK OF THIS GAZE CAN **KILL** AN ORDINARY MAN –

BELOW, IN THE MEZZANINE, THE FOURTH DARK JUDGE FLICKERS —

THEN HE TOO IS GONE!

IN AN UPPER APARTMENT, PSI-JUDGE **ANDERSON** SENSES THEIR DEPARTURE —

THEY'VE LAMMED OUT — JUDGE FEAR TOO! BACK TO THEIR OWN WORLD!

BUT FOR HOW LONG, ANDERSON? THEY'LL RETURN AGAIN UNLESS WE STOP THEM —

UNLESS WE FOLLOW THEM TO THEIR DIMENSION...AND **DESTROY THEM!**

ON JUDGE FEAR'S EMPTY SHELL, THEY FIND A STRANGE GLOBE – THIS IS THEIR DIMENSION JUMP! RECKON IT'LL TAKE US BOTH!

I HATE TO BE A PARTY POOPER, DREDD, BUT THESE CREEPS AREN'T EXACTLY GOING TO BE PUSHOVERS ON THEIR OWN GROUND!

WE'VE GOT NO CHOICE IN THE MATTER! READY...?

TOO LATE TO PUT IN FOR THAT SICK LEAVE, I SUPPOSE?

WE CAN **SQUEEEZZE** YOUR **SSSOUL** UNTIL IT **BLEEDSSS!**

*ANDERSON CLAWS THE EARTH IN HER AGONY — EARTH LITTERED WITH THE **BONES** OF THE **JUDGED** —*

AS THE SPIRITS OF THE FOUR DARK JUDGES ARE EXTINGUISHED, THE DEAD CARCASSES THAT HOUSE THEM — **CRUMBLE !**

IT'S OVER, DREDD ! THEY'LL NEVER TROUBLE US AGAIN !

THEY'RE STILL TROUBLING ME ! GIVE ME A HAND WITH THIS PITCHFORK, ANDERSON !

AFTER THIS, I THINK I'LL PUT IN FOR THAT SICK LEAVE !

AFTER THIS, I MAY JUST JOIN YOU, ANDERSON !

THE END

Cop these, creeps! The cataclysmic, collected mega-adventures of the ultimate lawman of Mega-City One, direct from the pages of *2000 AD*. Read and digest — or it's the iso-cubes for you!
Judge Dredd 1-22, The Cursed Earth 1-2, Judge Caligula 1-2, Judge Death, Judge Child 1-3, Block-Mania, Apocalypse War 1-2, City of the Damned, Judge Dredd in Oz 1-3.

GRAPHIC NOVELS

More than comic books, more than novels. The award-winning story-telling medium of the future — now, from Titan Books.
Choose from among: *Watchmen, Love and Rockets, Swamp Thing, The Woman Trap, Elfquest, Moebius, Heartbreak Soup, Superman: The Man of Tomorrow, The Return of Mister X, Ronin, The Shadow, Joe's Bar, The Last Voyage of Sinbad, The Magician's Wife, Camelot 3000.*